The Magic Reindeer

Text by Maureen Spurgeon
Illustrated by Stephen Holmes

KT-553-670

Brown Watson
ENGLAND

RONNIE the reindeer was always in trouble! "Oh, Ronnie!" cried Mother Deer. "How DID you get your antlers tangled up in this holly bush?"

"RONNIE!" roared Stag. "Why MUST you charge through the stream and splash water about? Look, I'm dripping wet!"

But as soon as Ronnie saw a bird in the sky or leaves rustling on a bush, off he'd dash. Then it would be, "Ronnie! Don't tread in our water!" or "Ronnie! You've splashed us with mud!"

All this made Ronnie feel very sad. If only he could do something really special, he thought, something to make all the other reindeer really proud of him...

Ronnie tried hard to think what he could do. But long after the other reindeer were asleep and night had fallen, he still hadn't thought of anything. He gave a big sigh, looking up at the sky.

Father Christmas was out on a practice sleigh-ride, ready for Christmas Eve. But Ronnie didn't know that. He was watching the reindeer flying! If they could fly, he told himself, he could, too!

Ronnie began practising the very next day. Off he went to the top of a hill. He took a deep breath, ran as fast as he could, then jumped, flapping his hooves about and hoping he would fly!

But flying wasn't nearly so easy as it looked! Ronnie just fell to the ground, squashing a clump of lovely, fresh grass! "Ronnie!" roared Stag. "You're getting into trouble AGAIN!"

Ronnie tried all sorts of things —
hopping about on each hoof,
jumping up and down... being
so busy and moving about so
much, he hardly noticed the
snow which had begun to fall...

And this time, before Ronnie could make a jump, his back hooves slid on the icy ground. Up he went into the air, his legs moving all at once. Ronnie could hardly believe it!

When Ronnie landed in the soft snow, he could see that he was quite a long way from where he had jumped - and that could only mean one thing! "I CAN fly!" he cried. "I can FLY!"

It was so exciting, Ronnie didn't want to stop! Again and again, he tried sliding on the snow, then lifting up his hooves and sailing through the air! "Look at me!" he cried. "I'm FLYING!"

Some of the other reindeer had already seen him! Off they went to tell Stag and Mother Deer about Ronnie learning to fly! But someone else had seen Ronnie, too...

"Oh, no!" groaned Father Christmas. "That little reindeer down there is trying to fly! And I thought EVERYONE knew that only MY reindeer can fly across the sky!"

Just then, Ronnie took another
jump, flapped his legs and his
hooves about, and fell down –
THUMP!
Poor Ronnie! He could not help
grinding his teeth in pain!

"I must do something about this," Father Christmas decided. "Steady, my reindeer. Let me get a sprinkle of stardust!" Soon, he knew, Ronnie would try to fly yet again.

Sure enough, the little reindeer
ran over the snow. Then he lifted
his legs, tucked in his hooves,
and... WHOOSH! Up he flew into
the sky in a shower of magic
stardust!

With stars twinkling and the moon shining, Ronnie could see all the trees and bushes, now far, far below. A cool wind blew on his hooves and his legs until they didn't hurt at all.

"Oh," said Ronnie, "now I know how it REALLY feels to fly!"
"You had worked hard, trying to learn," said Father Christmas. "You deserved to have your Christmas wish come true."

By now, the other reindeer had
called Stag and Mother Deer.
"Ronnie? Flying?" roared Stag.
"Rubbish! Where is he?"
"If he's got into trouble," said
Mother Deer, "I'll —"

But none of them ever knew what she would do. Because, at that moment, the moon came out from behind a cloud, making all the deer look up into the starry sky.

"It's Father Christmas!" breathed
the little reindeer.
"And his reindeer sleigh..." added
Stag, almost in a whisper.
"And RONNIE!" cried Mother
Deer. "He really CAN fly!"

Father Christmas guided his sleigh behind a mass of white, snowy cloud.

"Time for you to go, Ronnie!" he smiled. "This moonbeam will take you safely home."

Sliding down a moonbeam was as much fun as flying. "Thank you, Father Christmas!" cried Ronnie. "I hope I see you again!" "You will, Ronnie!" laughed Father Christmas. "You will!"

Ronnie landed safely on all four hooves. Now Stag, Mother Deer and all the reindeer wanted to hear about how he had flown with Father Christmas across the starry skies!